Peter's Railway
Activity Book

by

Christopher Vine and John Wardle

This activity book is based on the illustrations from the Peter's Railway series. They started out as the beautiful watercolours by John Wardle but, using a computer, I have carefully removed the colour content.

Most colouring books are just outlines, but the images here are a bit more helpful. I have tried to leave the pictures clear enough to colour in easily, but with a little hint for the young artist of how John used the colours to shade and highlight.

The colour section can be pulled out and used while working on the different pictures.

There are some other activities too. The gears quiz can be made with toy gears as an experiment and if anyone finds all of the differences in the pictures at the end of the book, they deserve a Gold Medal!

I hope you enjoy it.

Peter's Railway

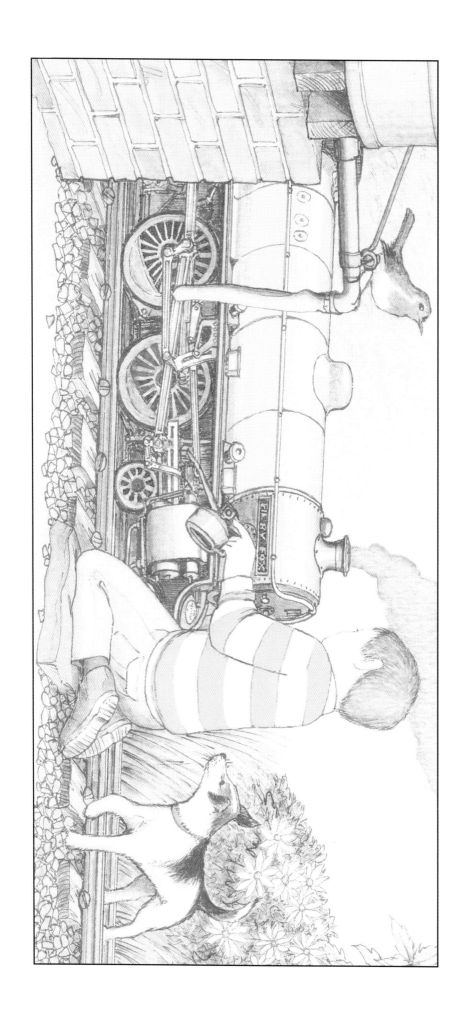

The cover picture from the first book in the series.

Peter is oiling up Fiery Fox before the first ever run on the new railway.

Heading for a picnic on the banks of the River Woe.

Wagons from the books

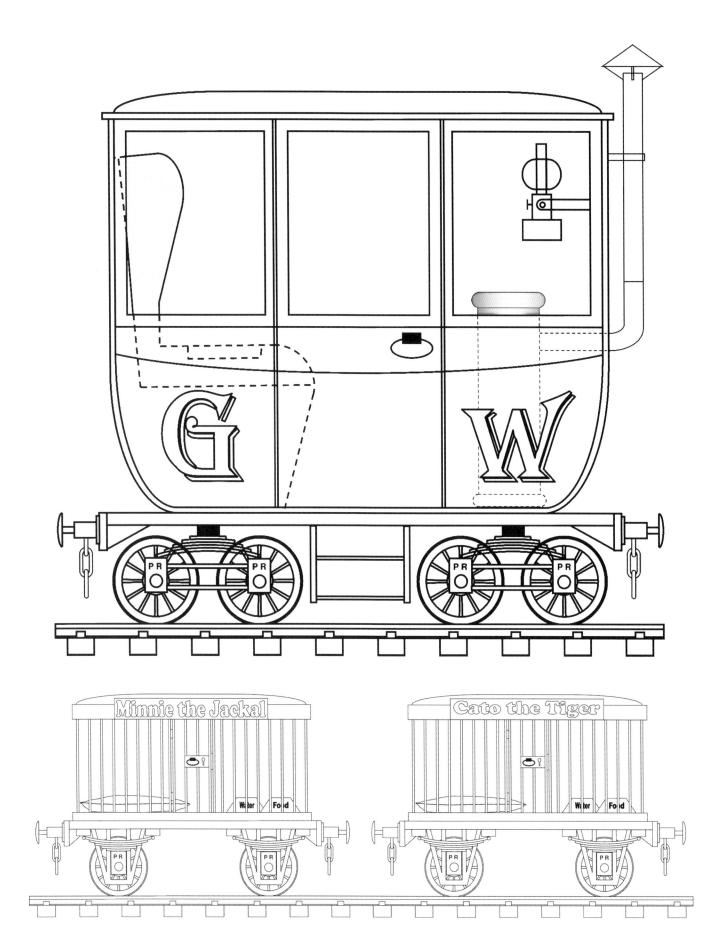

Modern electric power

The electric locomotive is hauling a freight train in Surprise Goods.
However an electric loco is not much use when there is a power cut.

A diesel engine goes up in smoke

This diesel locomotive has come to rescue the stranded secret train in
Surprise Goods, but now its engine has blown up.
The clouds of smoke from the exhaust show that all is not well.

A new electric locomotive

This is the moment of truth for Peter and Grandpa. Will it work?
The little locomotive has been built from scrap in Molten Metal.

Gear Puzzles

1. If gear A turns in the direction shown by the arrow, in which direction does gear B turn?

2. If gear A turns 10 times, how many times does B turn?

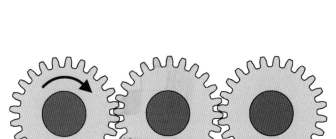

3. If gear A turns in the direction shown by the arrow, in which direction does gear C turn?

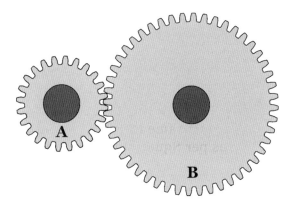

4. If you want gear B to rotate through one full turn, how many turns will gear A have to make?

Hint: It is useful to count the number of teeth on each gear.

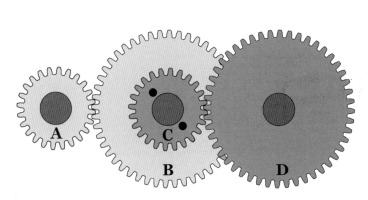

In this picture, gear A drives gear B which is connected to gear C. Gear C then drives gear D.

5. If gear D is to rotate through one full turn, then how many turns will gear A have to make?

6. If gear D drives a heavy load, will it be easier or harder to turn gear A?

Gears are explained more fully in Peter's Railway and the Forgotten Engine.

Crossword Puzzle

Across

1 Places trains stop at
3 Stephenson's famous engine
7 A quick look
9 Fastest steam locomotive
10 Protects a knight
11 You wait on these for trains
16 Stops trains at the end of a line
17 Wide awake and concentrating
20 American word for "railway"
23 Takes a line under a mountain
27 Name for a slope on a railway
28 Not small
29 It slows down a train or a bike
31 Rails sit on them. Night trains
32 Metal lines which trains run on

Down

1 It tells a train to stop and go
2 ----- clock will wake you up
4 Liquid which reduces friction
5 Finish
6 Track is bedded into these stones
8 The noise a steam locomotive makes
12 A string of railway vehicles
13 Not shut!
14 Electric ----- to turn machines and wheels
15 Colour of the lamp at the back of a train
16 A 4 wheeled truck and found up your nose!
18 The price of a ticket
19 Carries a line over a road or river perhaps
21 Turn this to adjust a machine or radio
22 Colour of the lamp at the front of a train
23 Carries coal and water behind a steam loco
24 Not heavy and useful at night
25 Train driver sits in here
26 Not arriving on time
29 Not a train, but does same thing on a road!
30 Short for Pounds per Square Inch, (pressure)

The Moonlight Express

Peter learns to drive Fiery Fox, under the Moon and stars.

Sausages at Yocketts Station

At the end of Christmas Steam, Grandma cooks sausages on a barbeque for all the passengers.

An excellent dream

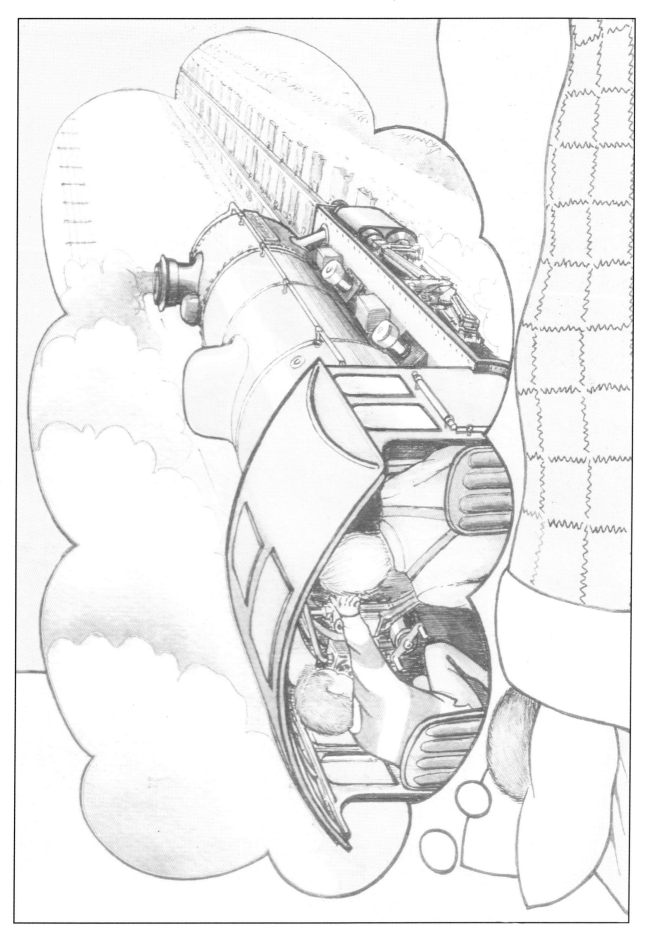

At the end of Peter's Railway to the Rescue, our young hero falls into a deep sleep. He and Grandpa have shrunk, or has Fiery Fox grown?

The curse of the Big Smellie Bogie!

On a dark night, unlucky engine No. 88 has run into rocks which have fallen onto the line. The driver and firemen pull the rocks out of the way and finish the journey without any brakes.
There was no Health and Safety in those days!

Mechanical destruction

Another disaster for No. 88 as the train hurtles down a long hill.
A coupling rod breaks and starts to smash the engine to pieces.

Shunting in A Dark and Stormy Night

The men at Hythe Station, shunting wagons on the running line.

Now and Then

Things have changed a lot in a hundred years.

Whoops!

The men in A Dark and Stormy Night made a series of mistakes.
A spectacular train crash was the result, but no one was hurt.

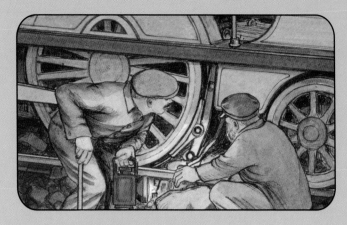

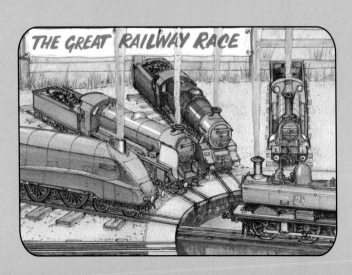

THE GREAT RAILWAY RACE

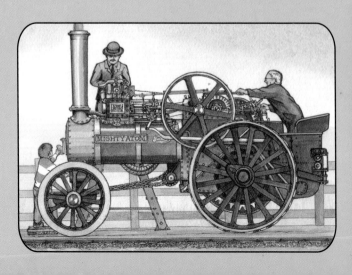

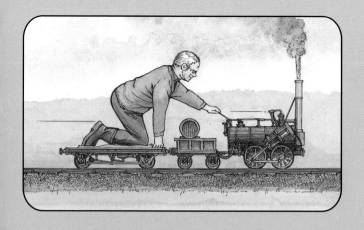

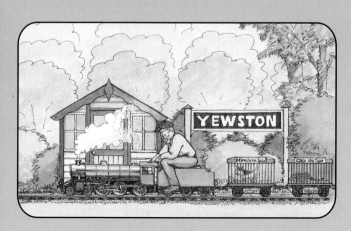

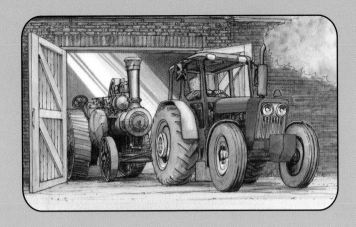

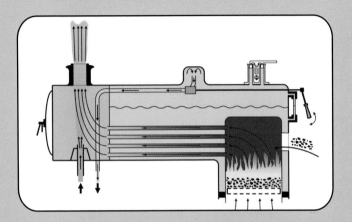

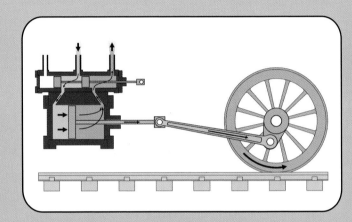

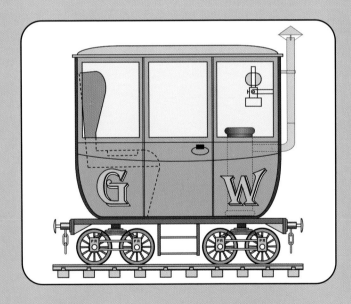

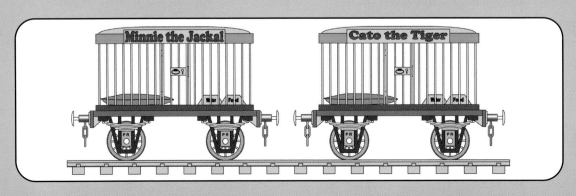

Boilers, Pistons and Cylinders

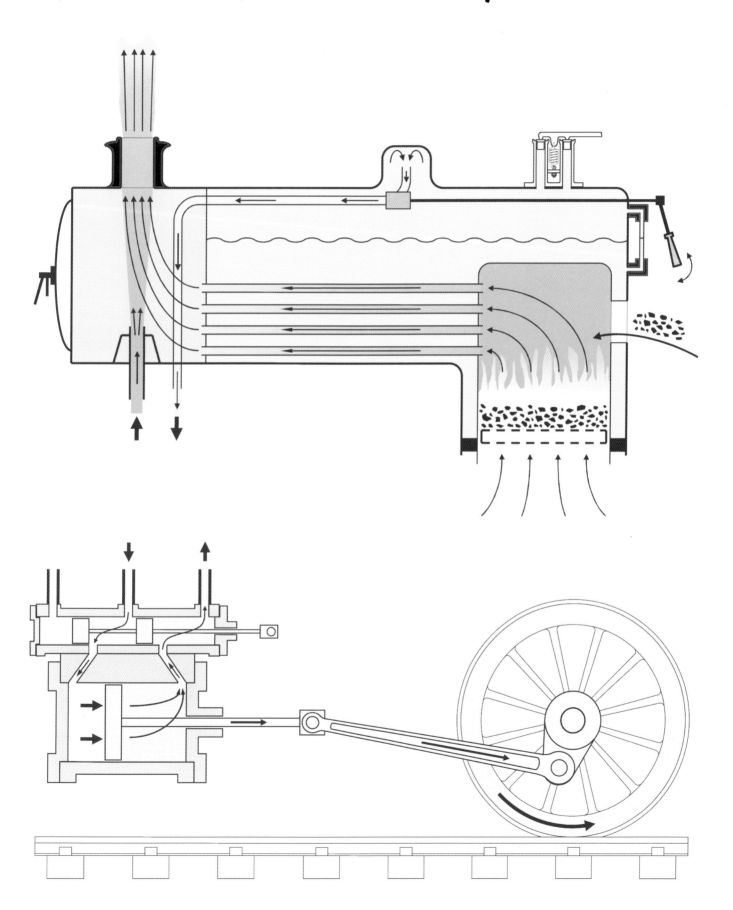

The Great Railway Race

All the competitors are getting up steam in The Forgotten Engine.
Who will win?

Peter racing

Peter is reducing his wind resistance to help Fiery Fox go faster.

An inspector calls on the Forgotten Engine

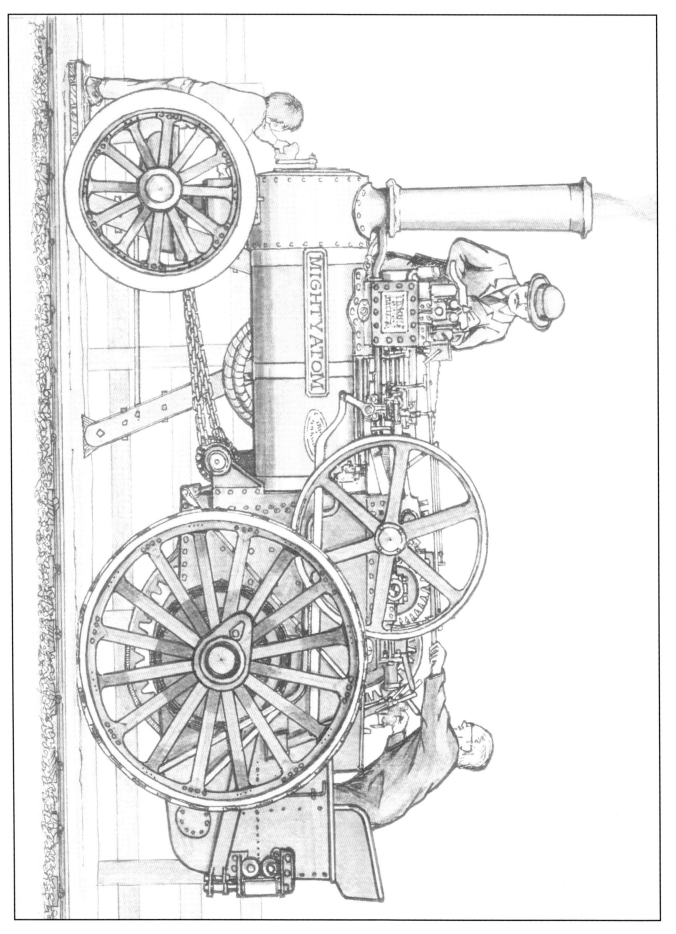

The boiler inspector making sure the boiler of Mighty Atom won't explode.

Invicta the old-timer

The white-haired old gentleman is driving Invicta very carefully in the race.

The steam car (mis)-adventure

Will Mr Mason's steam car be really slow? Poor Grandma is about to find out!...

Grandma nearly ends up in the River Woe

"Stop this thing at once!" shouts Grandma. "No Brakes!" Grandpa replies...

Cara drives Fiery Fox

It is Kitty and Harry's birthday in Surprise Goods.
Peter's friend, Cara, is helping to drive the engine and
blowing the steam whistle.

Word Search

Can you find the words in the grid?

BEARING
BOILER
CRANK
CUTTING
CYLINDER
DIESEL
EMBANKMENT
ENGINE
EUSTON
LOCOMOTIVE
PADDINGTON
PANTOGRAPH
PISTON
PRESSURE
SLEEPER
STEAM
WAGON
WATERLOO

```
M H C L Q D M H V E N U R P P
P A N T O G R A P H Y O Z A I
L B X F X C E Q P W B K G D S
E I O Q T N O R W T E N M D T
M I D I G N E M N H I S A I O
X V S I L S U E O T X I E N N
A O N S E M Z T T S I T G G
L E O U L K R U X Y I U S T N
X E R L N I C L F E Z V K O I
Z E S A R E D N I L Y C E N R
B Z B E P E N O T S U E K A A
P M V A I C T W A G O N D A E
E J P N O D A A C R A E B R B
K D W Z G H N D W R Z B X G W
S L E E P E R Z C R R Q M V J
```

In the Moonlight Express, Peter was given a cab ride in Green Goddess at the Romney Hythe & Dymchurch Railway.

Grandpa's workshop

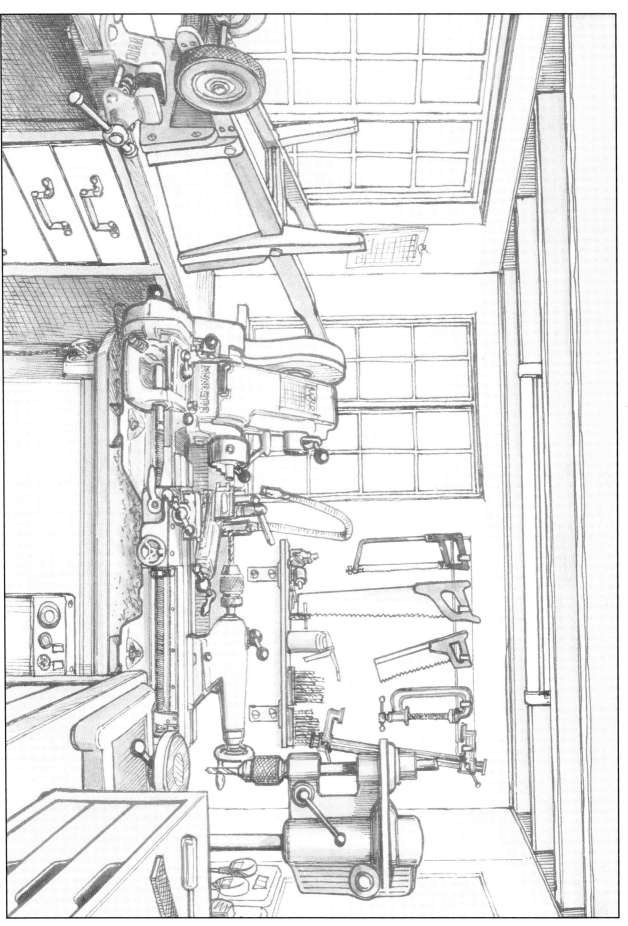

With the exception of Fiery Fox, Peter and Grandpa made everything for their railway in this workshop. Can you see a drilling machine, lathe, saws, files, clamps and a vice?

Yewston Station

This is the first arrival at Yewston station. Grandpa is driving and Minnie and Cato are in their special wagons.

Diggers, Tractors and Traction Engines

Burying the electric cable from the watermill to the farm.

Mighty Atom sees the light of day for the first time in fifty years.

Driving Mallard

Mallard is working hard in Surprise Goods. It takes a lot of coal to make enough steam to power her pistons and cylinders.
The driver is sitting on the left, with his hand on the reverser. The fireman is shovelling huge quantities of coal into the firebox.

Spot the Difference

Can you spot the differences between these two pictures of Bongo? There are 30. Some are easy to see, others very hard. If you can find them all, you are an eagle-eyed genius!

There is a special picture at www.petersrailway.com/activity.aspx which flicks between the images. Your brain makes the differences flash, as if by magic.

A modern diesel locomotive

From Now and Then, this is Now! 3300 Horse Power powered through the night.